WHERE ARE WE HEADED?

A BIOLOGIST TALKS ABOUT ORIGINS, EVOLUTION, AND THE FUTURE

by

JAN LEVER

Professor of Zoology, Free University, Amsterdam

Translated by Walter Lagerwey

WILLIAM B. EERDMANS / PUBLISHER
GRAND RAPIDS, MICHIGAN

215
LS·7w
83394
May 1973

Contents

I: TWO RELATED QUESTIONS

DURING THE FIRST HALF OF 1968 THE FREE UNIVERSITY OF
Amsterdam organized a number of public meetings — one
might call them teach-ins — in various cities in the Netherlands on the relationship between the findings of various
sciences and the Christian faith. Together with several
colleagues from the Faculty of Mathematics and Natural
Sciences I had occasion to discuss the question of how far
the results of research in the natural sciences can be recon-
ciled with the first chapters of the Bible.

Because of the great interest in these meetings, the many
questions that were raised, and the numerous critical
reactions that were expressed, the Netherlands Christian
Broadcasting Society asked me to discuss the problems involved in greater detail in a series of Sunday evening
broadcasts. I was happy to comply with this request and
gave nine short talks on the general subject of the Bible
and science. It is my sincere wish that the publication
of these talks will promote honest and open discussion by
Christians and non-Christians alike of the important issues
involved.

Since the questions we are dealing with involve the interpretation of the Bible, some people think it a disad-
vantage that I am a biologist and not a theologian. But
my being a biologist has the advantage of giving you an
opportunity to find out how an ordinary church member,
whose calling it is to labor in the area of the natural
sciences every day, reads the Bible and relates it to his
science. The Bible, you know, was written especially for
common, ordinary people like you and me.

The public discussions of this problem focused on two areas: first, the data available to us in the natural sciences pertaining to the age of the earth, the origin of life, the evolution of organisms, and the origin of man; second, the Genesis stories, which deal with creation and paradise. Thus the question concerning the interpretation of these scripture passages was central. Do they present an actual, exact account of events that took place in history? If not, what is their significance?

For some Christians the idea of changing their long held views about the first chapters of Genesis is frightening, not only because of their great respect for the Bible, but also because of their fear that a new interpretation would have consequences for the rest of the Bible, and that ultimately even the very essence of the gospel of Christ would be affected. Their unwillingness to accept the idea that the earth is billions of years old and that man's origins lie in the animal kingdom arises out of a concern that such ideas change the very essence of biblical revelation and the Christian faith. So they ask themselves, *Where are we headed* if we accept the views that are being set forth in the natural sciences? This is a good question and it deserves to be taken seriously.

The people who express this concern are often those who do not come into contact with the natural sciences in their daily occupation. But there are other people, also Christians, who have direct or indirect contact with the knowledge and insights of the modern natural sciences through their work. They are aware that great discoveries have been made in this area, discoveries that they cannot in good conscience deny. This is simply a matter of being honest. They, therefore, can come to only one conclusion, namely, that certain views regarding the origin of the world that have long been held in the Christian community must be wrong. These Christians surely do not reject biblical revelation and the gospel of Christ. On the contrary, precisely because they believe that the essential truths for life are to be found in the Bible, these Christians are of the opinion that another interpretation of its first chapters is not only necessary, but also possible and even enriching.

I wish to state at the outset that I hold this latter opinion. Please do not misunderstand me. I understand and am sympathetic toward those who hold the conservative position I have just set forth. Indeed, at one time I shared that point of view. Only after I had studied these problems intensively did my viewpoint change. Along with many other Christians I have found this change to be a liberating experience, because it opens one's eyes to the fact that the Christian religion — the gospel of Christ — has significance not only for his personal religious life, within the confines of the church, but that it also opens vistas on the great problems of our times and on the future of mankind.

This brings me to the second problem suggested by the title of this book: *Where are we headed?* I can well imagine that some non-Christians have already concluded that the subject of his book is really of no interest to them. Permit me to say that such a conclusion would be quite wrong. For the second problem that will engage our attention is of direct and immediate interest to Christian and non-Christian alike. The common question that confronts us when we look at the complex and in many respects terrifying world about us is: *Where are we headed?*

Never before has the future been so problematic for every individual as it is at the present time. Despite the rapid progress of technology during the past decades, and the many benefits we enjoy from it, there is the very real threat of total destruction through atomic power. Moreover, we are beginning increasingly to realize that our mismanagement of nature, the daily increasing pollution of rivers, lakes, and seas, the use of insecticides on an ever increasing scale, may very well radically and irrevocably upset the balance of nature one day. In addition, the enormous increase in the population of the world has caused such great mutual dependence and mutual responsibility among all men that the problems of space and food and reproduction affect us personally more than ever before. As a result of the penetration of communications networks (radio, television, etc.) to the remotest parts of the globe, we are often eyewitnesses to, and feel personally involved in, critical events — wars, revolutions, military and political suppression — at the very moment they are occurring.

Consequently, the individual's problems about his own little future are overshadowed by and absorbed in problems of the future that are of far greater magnitude. Gradually we are beginning to realize that there are no longer separate, individual futures, but that what is important is the future of all mankind. The questions concerning race, prosperity, peace, and freedom have become world problems for which purely local solutions are really no solutions at all.

There is still another important matter to consider. In the past it was common for institutions, points of view, and relationships to change very gradually. In fact, they changed so slowly that at times it actually appeared as if everything remained the same. Compare that to the world of today. Changes now occcur rapidly, so rapidly in fact that we have become aware that change is a characteristic of history. As a result, the question *Where are we headed?* becomes ever more urgent. And the consequence of all this is that often we have the feeling of being very trivial, very unimportant, that we are being swept along, as it were, by the terrific current of events. It is precisely such matters as these that together constitute the second problem we wish to discuss.

You may be wondering how the second problem, concerning the future of our world, is related to our earlier question about the interpretation of origins in Genesis and the future of the Christian religion. Is the linking of these two subjects in the question *Where are we headed?* not artificial and a mere play on words? We shall discuss this matter at length in the following chapters, but it may be useful to consider the relationship between these questions very briefly at the outset.

The accelerated rate of change that marks the present world has to a large extent resulted from the rapid growth of the natural sciences and the concomitant development of technology and medicine. Our entire life and a great share of our thinking, imagination, and fantasy are increasingly being permeated by the results, the ideas, and the methods of the natural sciences. Nevertheless, we are at a loss to know how to use the powers and the potentials that we have produced and hold in our hands. Consequently, there is a growing awareness that the greatest problems in our time are ethical and concern our view of the world and life. The knowledge explosion in the natural sciences calls for serious thinking on questions that are vital to all mankind. Christians are a part of mankind. They too must engage in this critical thinking. If the Christian faith — we might better say the gospel of Christ — has anything to say at this point, Christians will have to pass it on.

In these times, which are so strongly influenced by the natural sciences, it is absolutely imperative that Christians determine their position with respect to the knowledge and insights achieved in the natural sciences. We must be informed about the most important aspects of this knowledge and insight; we must be prepared, if necessary, to state clearly at certain points what, in our considered judgment, we cannot accept, but we must also be prepared to relinquish or to modify certain views that we have long held.

Now it is quite possible that someone will say: Please, let me be; let me keep the views I have; I am perfectly content with them; all those new ideas simply confuse me. Such a reaction is understandable, but I wish to urge you to read on. You simply cannot close your eyes to these problems, because you are constantly being confronted with them in newspapers and magazines, on the radio and television, and in conversations with others. For the sake of your children, who undoubtedly come home with a hundred and one such questions, it is very important that you know something about the problems, and that you arrive at a considered judgment about them.

It is especially with these people in mind, people who are often alarmed and disquieted by change in the church, that I wish to begin our discussion by dealing with questions of principle concerning the significance, the message, of the first chapters of the Bible. Only after that groundwork has been laid will we be ready to talk about the natural sciences.

We shall attempt to show something (in problems so
difficult one cannot and may not promise to do more) of
the role of Christian faith in its reflection on the problems
we have set forth above: Genesis and Science, and The
Gospel and the Future of Mankind.

II: PICTURES OF REALITY

In developing the theme WHERE ARE WE HEADED? I HAVE readers with three different kinds of religious backgrounds in mind. Such a classification is perhaps somewhat rigid, but I think it will be useful. The triple orientation will enable us better to probe in depth the problems being considered.

The first type of reader includes those Christians who believe that the entire Bible, every word of it, including the first chapters of Genesis, must be taken literally. Thus when one of the sciences sets forth views that conflict with the ones these Christians think they can deduce from certain words in the Bible, they conclude that this science must be wrong.

The second group includes Christians who are informed and knowledgeable about recent developments in the natural sciences and who have come to the conclusion that a literalist reading of the Bible cannot be maintained. The Bible, these Christians say, can be read in a nonliteral way without losing any of its significance, and indeed this must be done. A nonliteral reading, they claim, even enriches the insight and understanding a Christian may have of the origin and meaning of the world.

The third group of readers we wish to bear in mind are those who choose to be known as non-Christians or who, like certain humanists, would rather not be classified with Christians.

I would like to appeal to all three groups of readers and urge them strongly not to write each other off. All too often each group is only too ready to label the others as conservative, or dangerous, or pietistic, and then simply

13

to forget all about them. When we realize that all of us
are human beings, who during a short span of life ask
important questions about the origin, meaning, and pur-
pose of this earthly reality and of our own life, then at the
very least we should be prepared to listen to one another.

We can find a common point of orientation for all three
groups of readers by observing how their forefathers who
lived in Western Europe approached these questions
several years ago when science was still in its infancy. The
thinking of practically all people in that part of the world
was then dominated by Christendom. As far as their
knowledge of nature was concerned, these forefathers had
little more than daily experience to go by.

Everything they knew about the world was seen against
the background of the biblical narratives. This can be
clearly shown by a familiar example. It was generally
thought that the world was a more or less flat disk with
water underneath it around which the sun rotated. This
opinion was based on common sense experience; after all,
every day we see the sun appear, ascend, descend, and dis-
appear again. When doubts first arose concerning the accuracy of this naive, common sense world picture, it was
pointed out that this is the view expressed in many parts
of the Bible.

For a right understanding of our subject it is important
to realize that it was precisely at the time of the rise of
the natural sciences, between three and four hundred years
ago, that this common sense manner of interpretation was
raised to the level of a methodological approach, as is evi-
denced in the following examples.

When the first fossils — mostly petrified remains of organisms that had lived in the past — were found, some people
interpreted them as being the remains of plants and animals that had perished in the flood. Others were of the
opinion that these fossils had been formed by God *before*
he created living organisms.

When people began to raise questions about the age of
the earth, it was thought to be self-evident that it could be
calculated with the aid of the genealogical registers given
in the Bible.

When it was first realized that plants and animals could be divided into species, people drew the conclusion that obviously God had made these species — fully formed — during the creation week, and therefore they had to be constant.

When people began to observe the parasitic organisms that occur, for example, in the body of man and of his domestic animals, the question was raised in all seriousness: How could these organisms have come into existence? They are harmful and cause diseases; therefore, they could not have been made at creation, for originally it was "very good." These organisms must have come into existence after the fall even though creation had been completed by then. Some scholars solved the problem by assuming that originally these parasites were beneficial removers of superfluous wastes from the body of man, and that they did not become harmful until after the fall of man. Closely related was the commonly held conviction that death, disease, and deviation in nature, thus also in plants and animals, are all attributable to the fall of man in paradise.

Finally, when research on human sex cells was started, some people thought that these cells were really miniature human beings. Within these miniature human beings there were, of course, still other sex cells in which in turn, still smaller, the following generation of human beings was present, etc. These presuppositions were sometimes linked to the biblical account, for some people concluded that the successive generations of mankind were already present in the reproductive organs of Eve, enclosed within cells that became successively smaller. All mankind was, therefore, also present at the fall. From this still other theological conclusions could be drawn, for example, about original sin (or, as the Dutch has it, *erfzonde,* "inherited sin").

Thus at the very beginning of the development of the various natural sciences in modern times, we find a consistent pattern of linking scientific data and observations to biblical passages. This was true, as we have seen, for astronomy (the relation of sun and earth), geology (speculation about fossils and the age of the earth), biology (interpretation of the species), parasitology (origin of parasites), embryology (reproductive cells and generations), and medicine (origin of diseases).

This brings us to an extremely important point. It is imperative that we become fully aware of what our forefathers were really doing in reasoning thus and that we make a critical judgment about their reasoning. This awareness and this judgment are crucial as we form an opinion about the whole array of questions and problems that confront us.

Our forefathers very methodically linked the findings of the natural sciences in a given area to certain notions and statements in the Bible. Now what were they really doing? In order to clarify this we shall introduce the explanatory term "picture of reality." By this we mean the picture that we form of reality — of our world — on the basis of our knowledge and insights. Our picture of reality has reference, for example, to such questions as: Is the earth round or flat? Can animal species change? and the like. Thus, the concept "picture of reality" is much more objective than the concept "life and world view." This latter term has to do with the interpretation of knowledge, and on this Christians and non-Christians will have different views.

Our picture of reality always concerns what we know or think we know about this earthly reality. An obvious but important characteristic of it is that it changes. As science progresses our insight is enlarged and we must correct our notions about the world. In the various periods of the history of mankind pictures of reality have even displaced each other because of great discoveries that radically altered our insights.

Once this is understood, it suddenly becomes clear what our forefathers, whose views were presented above, were really doing. The Bible was written in times when people had far less factual knowledge about the world than we have. They had no telescopes, no microscopes, no laboratories. They knew nothing about electricity or about radioactive substances. As far as factual knowledge of the world is concerned, they had little more to go by than daily experience. It constituted the picture of reality of that time, now thousands of years distant. And it need not at all surprise us that the writers of the Bible also shared this

picture of reality, for their notions were completely em-
bedded in it.

At this point some will begin to object vehemently: "Yes,
but the Bible is divine revelation, isn't it? God inspired
the writers of the Bible to write." I also believe that. But
the Bible definitely is not concerned with scientific knowledge. The entire Bible was written within the framework
of existing notions about nature. The writers of the Bible
did not have scientific knowledge about astronomy, geology,
and biology.

But someone may say: "When you read the first chapters
of Genesis there is repeated reference to the sun, the stars,
all kinds of plants and animals, and the first human beings,
etc. So it does talk about all kinds of things that are the
object of scientific investigation at the present time. And as
you read, you certainly get the impression over and over
again that the writer is concerned to convey to us all kinds
of information."

Permit me to attempt to clarify this point again. Just
try to imagine that science and technology had made great
progress by the time the Bible was being written, that there
were universities, radio and television, refrigerators and
automobiles, airplanes and tanks, space flights and nuclear
power stations. Don't you suppose that if that had been the
case many expressions and pictures in the Bible would
have been different from what they now are, and that the
general knowledge about all kinds of things in nature
would also have been reflected in the biblical record? But
even if that had been true, then the perspective of faith,
our religious perspective on this earthly reality would in
no way have to be different from what it now is.

It would be extremely helpful if everyone would only
realize that the religious perspective of the Bible holds for
all time, even when it is conveyed in stories, concepts,
and pictures that are quite obviously characteristic of the
time in which the Bible was written. This common conviction would greatly reduce tensions and make possible
a liberating openness toward scientific discoveries. Only
through such openness can contact be established between
Christians and non-Christians in the increasingly numerous

controversies about the natural sciences in our time. How can a non-Christian put any trust in the Christian *faith* if Christians deny the clear and plain findings of the natural sciences?

III: FLAT OR ROUND

IN THE PRECEDING CHAPTER WE TOOK OUR STANCE AT THE cradle of modern science. We saw how our forefathers of several hundred years ago joined together the scientific data available to them with notions and ideas from the Bible. To clarify what was involved in this conjunction we introduced the idea of a picture of reality. Our forefathers arrived at this intertwining of their scientific knowledge with the Bible because their picture of reality was to a large extent still the same as that of the writers of the Bible. Scientific discoveries could, to be sure, at some points deepen perspectives of that picture. Any difficulties that might arise could more or less be smoothed over with involved arguments.

During the past few centuries, however, it has become increasingly clear that this was not a sound approach to the problems involved. At many points this long-standing, naive, common sense picture of reality began to collapse. The collapse already began when it was discovered that the earth is a sphere, that the sun does not revolve around the earth, but the earth revolves around the sun. As everyone knows, there was a great deal of controversy before this new view was adopted. No doubt, all of you now accept the view that the earth revolves around the sun. If that is indeed the case, then on a very important point you have replaced the Bible writers' naive picture of reality by the modern scientific picture. In doing so, you are saying that the naive picture of the writers of the Bible is simply wrong and that the Bible cannot be taken literally at this point. Furthermore, when we speak about divine revelation and the inspiration of the writers of the Bible, it is very clear that this does not pertain to this particular aspect of their picture of reality.

You will recall that in the first chapter I addressed my-self to three groups of readers. At this point we can well merge the first group with the second. To all of those in the first group, who hold to a literal understanding of the Bible, we can address the following questions: Do you think that the earth is round or flat? Does the sun revolve around the earth or does the earth revolve around the sun? If you answer these questions in accordance with present scientific opinion then you have taken a crucial first step in the direction in which other Christians — for the very same reasons — have taken many more steps. If you reflect carefully on this, you will also better understand what you are really saying when you ask the question *Where are we headed?* The *we* now pertains to you too.

Now if we agree that the earth is a sphere and revolves around the sun, we can proceed further and take a closer look at a number of other aspects of our picture of reality. Let us consider first of all the age of the earth. On the basis of the genealogies reported in the Bible, people used to think that the earth was about six thousand years old. Exact scientific research has shown that the earth is much older. One could even say that the earth is inconceivably old, because it comes to about five billion years. The methods for verifying the age of minerals and other objects often vary, but the results all point to and establish the accuracy of the conclusion that the history of this earth covers a much longer period of time than people used to think.

The same is true for the history of organisms. Life has existed on this earth for several billion years. We shall deal with this subject in greater detail in the following chapters. Suffice it to say here that man is much older than was formerly thought. His age may range from one to two million years. Just as we cannot deny that the earth is a sphere, so we cannot deny that the earth and all of its inhabitants are much older than was commonly thought in the past.

Much the same is true for the dying of organisms. We have already seen how people once thought that death, disease, and abnormalities could have occurred in organisms only *after* the fall in paradise. But the fact is that we know of countless numbers of fossils, the petrified remains of plants and animals, that lived before man was present on this earth. Incidentally, the frequently encountered opinion that fossils are rare is simply not true. Consider for a moment that in present-day society most of the energy and heat is obtained through the burning of fossils. Both coal and oil are derived from the remains of plants and animals that died eons ago. Consider also how many products, ranging from medicines to plastics, are made from these fossil materials. One could even posit that the whole modern development of mankind would not have been possible unless billions and billions of organisms had died before the coming of man.

Our forefathers, you recall, believed that the species of plants and animals are constant, so that they still look the same today as the day when God created them. This opinion, it now appears, is also wrong. Not only has fossil research proved that important changes did occur during the history of the world, but research on many present-day organisms has uncovered all kinds of mechanisms that trigger the process of evolution.

Let us now summarize our findings. In the examples we have considered, the conclusion was always the same: the old picture of reality is wrong. The earth is not flat, the sun does not revolve around the earth. The earth, the organisms, and man are not just a few thousand years old. Death in plants and animals did not originate after man's appearance on earth. The present species of organisms have not existed ever since the beginning of the earth, and they cannot be regarded as being constant.

Having discussed in greater detail these inadequacies in the attempts of our forefathers to relate scientific data with the common sense picture of reality found in the Bible writers, we are prepared to consider the whole matter of our changed, modern scientific picture of reality and its implications for faith.

If we can accept the fact that the earth is a sphere, then we can also accept without any objection the matters referred to in the above summary. In all honesty, then, we simply have to posit a new picture of reality to replace the old one of our forefathers. This means that we must give up the picture of reality held by the writers of the Bible. Only those who continue to insist that the earth is flat are consistent in rejecting modern scientific knowledge and thus also the new picture of reality.

Now when you give up the picture of reality of the writers of the Bible, is there anything left of the biblical message? The answer to this question is most emphatically *Yes*. The fact is that we can now understand its message all the better. It is precisely when we become aware of the contemporary aspects in the written record, that we can point out all the more clearly the distinctive character of the biblical message. This can be clearly demonstrated from the first chapter of the Bible. The writer was living at a time when the old picture of reality was held by all the people of the Middle East. In assuming this picture of reality, the writer was simply a child of his age. All the surrounding nations were very religious; they revered all kinds of gods and demigods, including local ones. All of these gods were from the world of nature — the sun, the moon, the stars, animals or men, or man-made images of them. People recognized sacred mountains, sacred trees, sacred animals, and the like. In short, these religions directed their worship, their prayers, their anxieties toward all kinds of things in this earthly reality, and brought sacrifices to these gods, often even human sacrifices.

In this dark age the author of Genesis 1 wrote a completely different story, a *confession* of the one God, who has brought forth this earthly reality. In this confession all the pseudo-gods of that time are downgraded to the level of creatures of this one God. The enumeration of them in Genesis 1 is complete. It takes all of reality out of the realm of the supernatural and reduces it to the realm of the secular. Considering when it was written, this is simply staggering. In sentence after sentence the writer deprives the gods of that time of their divine lustre. In the place of a world in which man anxiously suffers the domination of a whole web of pseudo-gods, Genesis presents us a clear and concrete reality that was and is for all times — also for the present — brought forth and governed by the one God. Read this chapter once again, bearing this in mind, placing yourself in the situation of the author.

Now I trust you can understand that absolutely nothing is lost when we realize that this confessional document is not at all concerned with communicating scientific information about the *exact* way the creation of the world took place. Such matters belong to the domain of science. We do wrong in attempting to find answers to such questions in the Bible. When we know, for example, that animals have existed for millions of years already, it is simply wrong to ask whether the "days" of Genesis have reference to long periods of time.

Genesis 1, we conclude, does not give us any scientific, historical, astronomical, or biological information. It is rather a grandiose confession of God who brought forth this reality and all that is in it. But the coming into existence of this earthly reality is by no means an autonomous or accidental event in the biblical confession. Although Genesis does not give us a picture of reality or scientific information about the world, it does provide us with the fundamentals for a *life and world view*, a religious perspective on the nature of this reality, its finitude and its dependence upon God in becoming and in being.

If this is rightly understood, it is also clear that in dealing with questions about the relation of the Christian faith to science we may never again, as did our forefathers, conjoin the picture of reality of the writers of the Bible in whole or in part with the data that are available to us on the basis of scientific research. The relation of Christian faith and natural science is on a much higher level. It occurs at the point where man, with all his scientific knowledge, in principle has no answers to his questions because they concern most profoundly the ultimate origin of reality, the ground and meaning of existence in general, and thus also of his own existence.

This implies that Christian and non-Christian alike can and indeed must have the same time-contingent picture of reality even though their respective life and world views, and thus their faiths, may vary greatly.

We shall conclude this part of our discussion with one

further illustration. If, on the basis of sufficient evidence, one were to conclude that his picture of reality must include the idea that man is the product of an evolutionary process (to be discussed more fully later), then a possible though not necessary proposition of a non-Christian life and world view might be that man was an accidental product in the evolutionary process and that conceivably he might not have come into existence at all. Conversely, a Christian will posit, following Genesis 1, that man is the focal point of evolution. This idea governs the Christian's perspective on all that relates to the origin and development of this earthly reality and gives it a distinctive coloration.

IV: PARADISE

IN THE PRECEDING CHAPTERS AN ATTEMPT WAS MADE TO SHOW what confusion resulted because Christians for so long failed to understand that the writers of the Bible accepted as a matter of course the picture of reality prevalent in their time. It was stated emphatically that the acceptance of the data and insights of the natural sciences, and thus of the present scientific picture of reality, is no more than an extension of the general acceptance of the fact that the earth is a sphere and revolves around the sun. Next, these conclusions were focused on the creation account in Genesis 1. We should not regard this story as an interesting account of historical events, but rather as a confession about God, who is the creator of all things in this earthly reality, and who therefore determines their being, their nature, their place, their meaning, and thus also their history. Moreover, it became evident, I trust, that in listening to the message — revelation — in this manner, nothing of the first chapter of Genesis is lost. On the contrary, the message can now be experienced in faith without the old tension between science and the Bible, since it clearly is valid for all times and is no longer obscured by conflicts between changing pictures of reality.

I am sure that readers from various Christian denominations who have been willing to follow the train of thought thus far are dubious about it just the same, because they sense that this approach has implications that go beyond those set forth so far. Consequently, they are not immediately prepared to proceed further along the path on which they have taken their first steps by accepting the fact that the earth is a sphere. For the moment that is expecting just a little too much from them.

That is why we must now speak about the paradise story. As a biologist I shall avoid the temptation to begin by introducing and discussing all kinds of scientific data about the origins of mankind in connection with this account. I must suppress this inclination precisely because the Bible — as we have seen previously — is never concerned with scientific data or a picture of reality. Unless this is clearly seen there is always the possibility that we shall lose the very essence, the revelation, the message of the Bible.

This then is also the point of departure for our discussion of the paradise account. Even as Genesis 1 is concerned with the dependence of all things in this earthly reality as the creatures of God, thus removing the pseudo-gods from their pedestals, so the paradise story deals with man in his relationship to God, his awareness of the existence of God, his realization of the will of God, his freedom to follow or to ignore the command of God, and his failure, in principle, on this very point.

Have you ever noticed how the paradise story depicts in an incomparable manner, with a minimum of words and metaphors, in a model as it were, the essence, the tragedy, and the hope of every human being? All the important moments and aspirations of human existence are here brought together in their purest form: the one God, the creator of heaven and earth, who reveals himself to man and speaks with him; the tree of the knowledge of good and evil as the manifestation of God's will and command; the tree of life, which points to eternal life; man, who is taken from the ordinary earth to this garden of encounter (read the story again on this point); mankind, represented by a man and a woman, cultivating and tending as the responsible earthly task of man; the snake representing all the cunning in the world; the temptation; the violation of God's command; the dawning consciousness of evil committed; nakedness as unmasking; the punishment, the tragic and meaningful being clothed with animal skins, but also the nontotal destruction of fallen man; and the hopeful prospect of an ultimate victory over all the deadly cunning in the world.

For a long time I shared the opinion that this story should be viewed simply as an account of definite historical events that took place somewhere on this earth in a little paradise in some distant past. This was the record, I thought, of a terrible event, which was experienced by two people, our first parents. Apparently it was only through the bonds of heredity that we were connected with this early history, the consequences of which we still experience.

Now there are many arguments to indicate that this interpretation of the story is inaccurate. These arguments, however, would take me into fields other than my own. I speak here only as a biologist who, like any ordinary Christian, wants to listen to the Bible. No involved theological and religio-historical arguments are required to make plain what the first chapters of Genesis are all about. Anyone who reads the Bible with common sense can reach the conclusion that a literal reading of the Genesis account is wrong. Permit me to illustrate this briefly with a comparison of two passages, in Genesis 1 and 2 respectively.

When the fifth day of creation is discussed in Genesis 1 we read: "So God created the great sea monsters and every living creature that moves, with which the waters swarm, according to their kinds, and every winged bird according to its kind" (Gen. 1:21). When the sixth day comes up for discussion we read: "And God made the beasts of the earth according to their kinds and the cattle according to their kinds, and everything that creeps upon the ground according to its kind" (Gen. 1:25). Then, next and last, is man: "So God created man in his own image, in the image of God created he him; male and female he created them" (Gen. 1:27).

Now if we next turn to Genesis 2 we find a second creation account, which has no reference at all to days. This account begins with the creation of man; next the Garden of Eden is planted; then it says: "So out of the ground the LORD God formed every beast of the field and every bird of the air" (Gen. 2:19); finally woman is formed. These two passages quite plainly contradict each other. In the first, man and woman are mentioned last; the second begins with man, then follow the animals of the field, and the birds, and woman is mentioned last.

If you take the older point of view, namely, that these passages must be read literally and therefore concern actual events, then you can only conclude that one of the accounts must be wrong. Both cannot possibly be correct. Still, there they are, the two stories, the one following directly upon the other in the Bible, as if there were nothing unusual about them at all. The only conclusion to which we can come is that quite obviously these chapters do not aim to give a report of events that took place then and there.

The paradise story is concerned with the essential and deepest problems of the individual, and of all men, from the first man on. Always, since the first beginning, man has stood over against God in a tension of good and evil. Evil has affected man's life. In all of history he has constantly made wrong choices.

But, someone will say, from these first chapters we have always gotten the impression that creation was good in the beginning, without evil and death among men or animals. Here we touch upon a problem that we humans cannot solve. Why do evil and death exist in the world? This is a mystery that defies our powers of comprehension. Nor do the Genesis accounts solve it; they only proceed on the basis of this diagnosis. Indeed, the paradise story was written to make this diagnosis of the human situation. Bear in mind that even those who have viewed this story as event have not known how to cope with the serpent. How could it be so wicked before man had fallen? After all, the animals were created good, were they not?

Similarly, death, which is central in the paradise story — "For on the day that you eat of it, you shall die" — quite clearly did not refer to the mortality that is characteristic of all of life. Man in the paradise story did not actually die on the day that he ate of the tree. About what death is the paradise story talking then? We can understand that better if we listen carefully to the gospel of Christ in the New Testament. For that matter, the entire paradise story is illuminated by the gospel. In one of his talks Jesus says: "I am the living bread which came down from heaven; if any one eats of this bread, he will live forever" (John 6:51).

In other words, those who follow Jesus and thus act according to God's will, will live forever. And still all of Christ's
followers die. Thus both the paradise story and the words
of Jesus have to do not with ordinary death, the termina-
tion of biological life, but with something quite different.
Both passages are concerned with whether man makes or
misses contact with God and the destiny God has for him,
whether or not he has a part in the future, both during
his own life and in that more distant future we call the
hereafter, which is still mysterious and hard to understand,
in which we can only believe, and which is in fact indicated
by the terms *new world* and *re-creation*.

The paradise story, like that of creation, has profound
meaning and dramatic religious significance. It is written
out of faith and on behalf of faith. It concerns the deepest
questions and conflicts in the life of every man in all times,
and deals with God's intentions for the earthly reality that
he made. By referring the paradise story back in time and
reducing it to the account of a single event that took place
in one small spot on the globe and involved just two people,
particular trees, and one speaking snake, one greatly im-
poverishes the significance of the story. In past centuries
Christians have stared themselves blind at details in Genesis
and we have had disputes about them in the churches. As
a result we have often lost sight of the staggering riches of
the illuminating vision of faith in the paradise story.

Newer insights into the creation story, the paradise story,
and the rest of the Bible, including the New Testament, do
not undermine the essence of the Christian faith, but
rather enable us to understand the faith and its demands
on us and on all of mankind all the better. These insights
free us from many pseudo-problems and pseudo-solutions,
from endless and fruitless discussions that only waste time,
and in general from an atmosphere of dissatisfaction and
suspicion. By removing the obstacles caused by our short-
sightedness, these new insights once again open the way
for all to see the far-reaching significance of the biblical
message for the world of today and of tomorrow. I repeat,
for *all* to see, for adults, for the youth of the church — and
for those who are not yet Christians.

Back to paradise. What stirs our deepest longings when

we read this story? The tree of life. Did it drown and die
in the flood? On the last page of the Bible we read: "Blessed
are those who wash their robes, that they may have the
right to the tree of life and that they may enter the city by
the gates" (Rev. 22:14). Was paradise only a tiny spot somewhere in the East that vanished in the flood? In the horror
of the crucifixion story we read: "One of the criminals
who were hanged railed at him, saying, 'Are you not the
Christ? Save yourself and us!' But the other rebuked him,
saying, 'Do you not fear God, since you are under the same
sentence of condemnation? And we indeed justly; for we are
receiving the due reward of our deeds; but this man has
done nothing wrong.' And he said, 'Jesus, remember me
when you come in your kingly power.' And he said to him,
'Truly, I say to you, today you will be with me in Paradise' "
(Luke 23:39-43).

V: THE ORIGIN OF LIFE

WE HAVE SEEN THAT IT IS POSSIBLE TO INTERPRET THE FIRST chapters of Genesis differently from the way many people have been reading them for a long time. It has become evident that the new nonliteral reading can make us more open to modern science and the present-day picture of reality. Once we realize that the religious message in these chapters can be dissociated from the framework provided by the picture of reality of the writers, then we may quite possibly become very eager to know the view of present-day scientific thought concerning the origin of this earthly reality. To this subject we shall now turn our attention. At the same time it is our intention to show that the Christian faith, the gospel of Christ, is not old-fashioned or irrelevant to this modern world, but that it can be of vital significance, especially with an eye to the future.

However, before we can pursue this line of thought, there are two questions that are so important that we shall have to consider them first. These questions concern the origin of life on earth and the origin of man. In this chapter we will discuss the origin of life; in the next the origin of man.

Interest has been focused on the origin of life throughout the history of western civilization, beginning with the Greeks. Initially, attention was centered almost exclusively on questions pertaining to the origin of this *present* life. Naturally, people knew that in all kinds of organisms new generations come into existence through birth or develop out of eggs. But it was also thought that many new organisms originate, ever and anew, from lifeless matter. On the basis of observation, people thought that this was true, for instance, of fish, worms, insects, salamanders, and mice.

31

Because their methods of investigation were not sufficiently refined, they were unable to discover the actual processes involved and instead believed that everywhere in nature new life arose spontaneously from lifeless matter. Accordingly, this process was called *generatio spontanea*, or spontaneous generation.

When this scientific view of generation was subsequently confronted with the Christian faith a conflict developed. After all, creation had taken place long ago. How then was it possible for new living creatures spontaneously to come into existence? Augustine proposed one solution to this problem by suggesting that at the time of creation innumerable, invisible, tiny germs of all kinds of organisms were formed. After creation they did not all emerge at the same time, but they remained present everywhere in large numbers. Augustine's view suggests that it is not really spontaneous generation that occurs when new life comes forth, but rather that the new life is a development of previously created germs. By taking this point of view he resolved this conflict between Christian faith and science.

It would take us too far afield to discuss in detail the interesting history of the idea of spontaneous generation. Suffice it to say that exact investigation of the problem began in the seventeenth century, and it soon became evident that the long held view of spontaneous generation was wrong. Nevertheless, it was not until the second half of the nineteenth century that scientists reached the conclusion that none of our present-day organisms can develop from lifeless matter. Only life produces life.

Another question now began to stir a great deal of interest. What was the origin of the *first* life on earth? The question first arose because scientists had discovered that the earth was much older than had long been thought. Moreover, the study of fossils revealed that in the past organisms had lived that were very different from those now existing. Looking back in time, scholars saw, as it were, the history of the process of the formation of the present plant and animal worlds. This led to the further conclusion that this process of development exhibited an evolution from lower to higher. This in turn led to the idea that the development of life on earth must have started with very simple organisms, and that these in turn must have developed from lifeless matter, since there was no life on our planet when it first came into existence. This conception, which grew out of the theory of evolution, was at the outset wholly hypothetical, an idea for which no scientific arguments could be adduced.

After World War II a great number of discoveries were made which gave this hypothesis plausibility. Let us look at some of these.

First of all, it has become evident in modern investigation that all present living organisms display a very high degree of agreement and even identity in their most basic life characteristics and structures. Everyone knows that the bodies of plants, animals, and men are built up out of cells. In this, then, they are strikingly alike. Now with the aid of highly refined apparatus it was possible to gain much valuable information about the structure and function of these cells. It became evident that the most important substances in all cells are two types of long molecules called nucleic acids and proteins. We can picture these substances as strings wth a large number of differently colored beads. Among the nucleic acids there are four kinds of beads, among the proteins there are twenty different kinds. The function of these strings is very important. Inherited characteristics, like the color of your hair, the shape of your nose, but also aspects of your character, are fixed in the arrangement of the four types of beads in the nucleic acids in our cells. In a comparable way all processes in our cells (muscle, nerve, intestinal cells, etc.) are governed and controlled by the precise, sequential arrangements of the twenty types of beads in the proteins.

Thus there is present in the cells of all organisms the same relatively simple and very schematic basic life principle. That was a startling discovery. Moreover, it was found that in all cells of all organisms the energy substance — we may conveniently call it fuel — is produced and used up in exactly the same chemical compound.

Now you may say, "But what does all that have to do with the question about the origin of life?" That we must still consider.

In recent years scientists have gotten an impression of

the conditions on the surface of the earth several billions of years ago when there was no life present. There were oceans then, but the atmosphere was different. On the basis of various arguments, which we cannot enter into now, scientists have concluded that the air then contained very little oxygen and carbon dioxide, if any. However, other gases, such as ammonia, were present.

Scientists then reproduced this primordial condition in their apparatus and exposed it to ultraviolet rays like those present in sunlight and to other factors operative in nature. A surprising discovery was made. Without life being present, a great variety of organic substances began to develop, including all the substances that, as we have already seen, occur in the cells of all living organisms — the beads of the nucleic acids, the beads of the proteins, and also the energy substance to which we referred.

This observation, necessarily dealt with in a most cursory way here, led to the view that several billion years ago the oceans gradually developed into a kind of soup, full of substances vital to life. From experiments done in recent years it now appears that under certain conditions small spherical bodies develop that exhibit a few of the characteristics we ordinarily associate with life. In short, it cannot be denied that the natural sciences are presently tracking down the origin of the first life on earth.

Perhaps you have been reading this with mounting alarm and concern. For if we must conceive of the origin of life on earth as taking place through natural causes by the sun's impact on substances that can be bought at any drug store — or to go even further, if man may succeed in making life in a test tube — then what remains of faith in God as the creator of life? Is science really saying that God is not the source of life, but that we must substitute the oceans for God? Isn't that just plain materialism that shoves aside creation and makes it impossible?

These questions arise from the notion that belief in creation implies that God in the course of the creation week reached down from above, as it were, several times in order to add completely new things out of "nothing." This view follows in part from the classical interpretation of Genesis 1 which, as we saw in our earlier discussion, is wrong. In part this view is also philosophical in its origin.

But we can also approach these problems in a very different and far more fundamental way. Increasingly, it is becoming clear to us, in view of our increased knowledge about living organisms, that this earthly reality is *one*, also in its origins. This thoroughly interrelated reality is, we believe, the creation of God. The Creator does not intervene locally or temporally; on the contrary, the whole of it is always and everywhere his creation. The primal oceans were the source from which life could come forth because the Fountain of Life held the oceans and life in his creative hands — to use a figure of speech that is readily understood.

"Creation" is, therefore, much more powerful, much more all-embracing than we used to think when we reduced and diminished it to acts that occurred at a particular time and place. If in the future we should succeed in making a simple, living organism in our laboratories, then we will not have demonstrated that God is not the creator; rather we will be filled with awe and wonder at the possibilities present in creation and, no less, at the powers God has given to man in this earthly reality. For is it not remarkable that in this reality, in this creation, a living creature occurs, also made up of matter, also consisting of nucleic acids and proteins, who can and may do so much, who is so determined and yet so free, and who, moreover, is conscious of his being as a creature? The origin of this man is the subject of our next chapter.

VI: THE ORIGIN OF MAN

ALTHOUGH THE PROBLEM OF THE ORIGIN OF LIFE ON THIS earth, which we discussed in the last chapter, is surely an interesting one, without a doubt the question about the origin of man is even more intriguing to us. For this latter question concerns all of us, you and me, and our relationship to the rest of the creation of which we are a part.

According to the writers of the Bible, we human beings are wholly a part of the created reality. In our origin we are not gods or demigods descended to earth, as was believed by so many ancient peoples. We read in Genesis: "Then the LORD God formed man of dust from the ground, and breathed into his nostrils the breath of life; and man became a living being" (Gen. 2:7). A little further on we read: "In the sweat of your face you shall eat bread till you return to the ground, for out of it you were taken; you are dust, and to dust you shall return" (Gen. 3:19).

In the past these statements were understood to mean not only that man is a real part of the entire creation but that God, like a potter, literally formed man out of dust and clay. Because of this literal interpretation many people who later were willing to accept the idea of evolution within the plant and animal kingdoms nevertheless insisted on making an exception for man. Man, it was said, must have been created independently and wholly apart from other organisms. Some, especially in Roman Catholic circles, went even further, positing that the body of man could have been produced through evolution, but that the soul is added later by an act of creation repeated for every individual.

In previous chapters we have repeatedly seen how many errors have been made through such literal interpretations

36

of biblical texts. For that reason, we do well first to examine what kind of scientific data are available to us concerning the origin of man.

Let us then begin with a comparison of present-day man with present-day organisms. In the last chapter we saw that the fundamental processes and structures of all organisms manifest a striking similarity. In not a single respect is man an exception to this generalization. The basic life processes we have in common with plants, snails, beetles, fish, and mice. For example, our heredity mechanism, by which generations are linked to each other, is the same as that of our fellow creatures.

Furthermore, when we observe the structure of our body, it appears that we belong to the group of vertebrate animals, in particular to the mammals. We possess all the organs present in them. Our manner of reproduction and of feeding the young is the same. If we extract hormones from the organs of animals and inject these into our bloodstream, the same reactions occur in us as do in the animals. In short, at this level we correspond entirely to the animals.

In addition, we are absolutely tied to lifeless matter. By breathing and feeding we take in the molecules and the atoms that must form our body. We are made up of the same carbon, oxygen, nitrogen, chlorine, iron, copper, magnesium, etc., as are all other organisms. For the most part, these atoms have functioned countless times before in other plants and animals. We are thoroughly a part of this earthly reality and our bodies consist of temporal combinations of ancient matter.

We correspond most to the anthropoid apes, of which there still exist the chimpanzee and gorilla in Africa and the orangutan and gibbon in Asia. Our resemblance to these animals strikes us every time we see them in a zoo. Still, some clear differences can be pointed out. The anthropoid apes have thick bone walls, eyebrow walls above the eyes; a real forehead is not present; the weight of their brains is much smaller than ours; their set of teeth is heavier and curved somewhat differently; and they do not have a bony chin on the lower jaw. Another striking difference is their walking on four feet, reflected in many characteristics of the skeleton, for example, the position of the cranium with respect to the spinal column and the shape of the pelvis.

When the theory of evolution was first proposed in the nineteenth century, it included the idea that man had come forth from the animal kingdom. Initially it was thought, however, that man had developed from the group of anthropoid apes that we still find today. Comparisons were made at many points and in the end, you might say, the chimpanzee "won out." Since then, however, our view of this problem has changed considerably because of excavations that have been made in various parts of the world.

Space limitations permit the mention of only a few of the most basic points. A first conclusion to which the investigations led was that the present anthropoids are the late descendants of a group of animals that embraced many more species and existed for millions of years alongside another line that eventually led to man. Thus it is out of the question that we should have descended from one of the four types of apes still to be seen in our zoos.

Accordingly, the question concerning the origin of man has been focused increasingly on other fossils, especially those in deposits formed during the past one to two million years, the familiar period of the ice ages. The evidence also indicates that in the past a much greater variety of human types and man-like forms existed than had been previously suspected.

Mankind at present forms a single biological species; after all, crossings between all races are possible. This species is called *Homo sapiens*. He has been in existence for more than 100,000 years. During the last ice age and somewhat before, a divergent type of man existed, the so-called Neanderthal man, who had a forehead that slanted backward and bone ridges above the eye sockets, and who lacked a bony chin. These people, of whom hundreds of fossils are known, looked more like the anthropoid apes than we do. Their cranial capacity, however, was just as great as ours. Many of the stone tools they made are also known to us. We also know that they sometimes buried their dead.

Much older are the so-called Pithecanthropus forms. These date back about 250,000 to 600,000 years. A rather large number of their fossil remains have been found in

various places in Asia and Africa. They had hardly any
forehead, and their cranial capacity was considerably smaller
than that of present-day man. They looked even more like
anthropoid apes than the Neanderthals. Nevertheless, they
also left cultural remains that are known to us.

During the past several decades many remains of organisms have been found, especially in South and East Africa,
which date back to the beginning of the ice ages, between
600,000 and 2,000,000 years ago. In their skeletons they
display a remarkable mixture of human and anthropoid
features. Of these we also know several types, some with a
heavy longitudinal bony crest on the skull, as is the case
with anthropoid apes, but also forms in which this is absent,
as in man. The cranial capacity of these organisms was just
a little above that of present-day apes. They walked up-
right on two feet. From those ancient times we also have
stone implements, often found together with bones of these
organisms. From even older layers we have forms that, struc-
turally, could well have been the ancestors of these remarkable organisms.

The interpretation generally given to these finds today is
that the line leading to man has been different from that
leading to the present anthropoid apes for millions of years
already. In our line there existed initially numerous pre-
sumably animal forms that have for the most part died out
as side branches. These forms looked even more like us
than do the recent anthropoid apes.

In this thicket of forms the human form gradually took
shape. As far as body structure is concerned, it came to
expression especially in increasing cranial capacity. The
real central human line also had later side branches, such
as the Neanderthal man, but only *Homo sapiens,* present-
day man, remained.

We have referred in passing to cultural remains. Quite obviously, that is a very important point, for present-day man
distinguishes himself from all other living creatures by his
culture. However, when we trace cultural origins we find
that they become fewer as we move back in time. The famous
cave dwellings found in France and Spain date back to the
end of the last ice age, more than 10,000 years ago. From
that period we have all kinds of objects made by *Homo*

sapiens, and some from even before that time. These include images, jewelry, whistles, and tools, among them fish hooks, needles, knives, saws, and drills, made from stone or bone and serving many different uses. There is also evidence of burial rituals. If we go back even further into the period of the ice ages, we find almost exclusively stone implements. The older they are, the simpler, and if we go back about one or two million years we find that they are no more than pebbles from which pieces have been struck off.

The impression we get from these findings is that culture began very weakly, became stronger in the course of hundreds of thousands of years, with the result that it was not until about the time of the last ice age that *Homo sapiens,* our species, finally became fully developed.

Summarizing, we can say that it has become evident that our body in its most fundamental processes works exactly like other organisms. We possess the same organs as do the mammals, and in many respects we most resemble the present anthropoid apes; however, we do not descend from them. Rather, the data point to a line of creatures, separate for millions of years, leading to man. From this line, which had many side branches, *Homo sapiens* finally emerged. Lastly, that culture which is so characteristic of man gradually got under way.

For some readers the material presented in this chapter on the origin of man contains nothing new. But for many others it must be most shocking. If your parents, teachers, and preachers talked only about the first chapters of Genesis when the subject of the origin of man came up at home, in school or in catechism, then you may well have gotten the impression that the foundations of our Christian faith are being swept away by such modern views as these.

But if we believe that God has created this earthly reality, then surely it is a good thing for us to find out what the natural sciences have discovered about the origin of this reality, his world. Then it is also right and necessary for us to change and modify the conceptions and pictures we have formed in the past. For if we do not, we shall have a wrong picture of created reality. Frequently, though, it is very difficult for us to change and modify our ideas and opinions.

Often we are so stuck in a rut that we become a stumbling block to progress.

In conclusion, then, one final reference to the origin of man. Although we shall return to this subject in a broader context, there is one question I would like to pose now. In view of the profound religious meaning of the pertinent biblical passages, does it really make any difference whether we conceive of God as having formed man out of *the dust of the earth* or whether he made man come forth from *the highest living organisms?* Personally, I really find the latter view much more beautiful. As a biologist I know something of how incredibly marvelous is the structure of these creatures.

VII: CONSCIOUSNESS

IN THE PRECEDING CHAPTERS WE HAVE BEEN DOING PREPARA-
tory work, laying a foundation on which we could attempt
to develop a coherent, total view. We have seen that the
writers of the Bible, whether they were Old Testament
Hebrews or New Testament Christians, expressed their
divinely inspired view of this earthly reality in words and
notions that were strongly influenced by the prescientific
picture of reality of their time. We have also ascertained
that this picture of reality has proved to be wrong on nearly
every point. Finally, we discussed at somewhat greater
length contemporary scientific data and views on two very
crucial questions, the origin of life and the origin of man.
We now wish to discuss the following question: If we
adopt the present scientific picture of reality, will there be
anything left of our Christian faith; and, if there is, can it
still be of any significance?

Now it is obvious that I shall have to limit myself in discussing these questions. As a biologist I cannot encroach
on the fields of theology and philosophy. So I am speaking
as a natural scientist of our time, using the language and
the pictures of the natural sciences. As concerns the Christian faith, I simply take my stand on the most basic Christian beliefs — that God is the creator of the entire earthly
reality, that mankind was infected with evil, beginning with
our first parents, and that the way to the Creator and to
peace on earth can be found in Christ in whom God has
revealed himself.

For those who believe that God is the creator of this
entire earthly reality, the process of evolution described by
the natural sciences in the present-day picture of reality

becomes a grand manifestation of God's intentions and activities. Just as the embryonic development of the fertilized human egg cell, which occurs entirely according to the laws of nature, can be experienced by us as a great marvel, so that we stand in awe and wonder before our Creator at the birth of a child, so we can have this same experience when we view the development of life on earth in accordance with the present-day picture of reality. Let us try to experience something of this together.

About five billion years ago, through some astronomical event in the solar system, the earth came into existence. In the course of time the continents and oceans were formed. There were seasons and tides, weather and wind. But living creatures did not yet exist. The earth was uninhabited and barren. Sea water was sterile from top to bottom. The composition of the atmosphere was different from what it is today, lacking oxygen and carbon dioxide.

Then over the course of millions of years something began to change. Sunlight and lightning and radioactive rays brought about chemical reactions that caused some very specific organic substances to develop. These organic substances, because of their properties, were combined into larger units. In all likelihood this process took place along the coasts, where at low tide the temperatures are high because of the sun's heat and the occasional flow of hot lava from volcanoes into the sea. In the course of millions of years "little things" finally originated, able to grow and divide, to absorb materials out of the sea water, and to give off other substances. In short, in a marvelous manner an entirely new and higher facet of creation appeared: life. Life differentiated itself, depending on all kinds of circumstances, into a variety of forms. A few billion years ago bacteria and algae, comparatively simple organisms, existed, as we can tell from fossils. The first forms of life fed on all the organic substances that had developed during the preceding centuries. It is very likely that the composition of our atmosphere also changed during this period. Metabolism, to which we just referred, must have been a form of fermentation. Thus the oceans fermented and carbon dioxide, which we still find in air and water, originated. Thereafter small green organisms developed which, like the plants of our day, caught and used a portion of this carbon dioxide with their green leaves. In this process oxygen develops. Rising from the sea water in little bubbles, oxygen also got into the air, and thereafter it was used by many of the newly developed organisms as breathing processes appeared.

The organisms that had developed up to this point were all herbaceous, but then in some way that we still do not wholly comprehend, animals also developed in the sea. There are many fossils of numerous kinds of marine animals, dating back from 500 to 600 million years ago. It should be clearly understood that animal life again constituted another and higher phase in this earthly reality. After all, animals have senses and a nervous system. At this stage certain components in this earthly reality obtained senses: they began to taste, feel, and see other parts of reality and other organisms. Thus there occurred, as it were, a process of awakening.

Various types of animals were able to adapt to a lower salt concentration and entered fresh water by way of the river mouths.

A very important type of animal, the vertebrates, was still lacking. These originated about 400 million years ago, very likely in the form of jawless creatures in fresh water. This group is now practically extinct. Then followed, about 100 million years later, the fish that populated the fresh water and the sea in an enormous variety of forms. Still later followed the amphibians — salamanders, frogs, and toads. This means that vertebrate animals must now for the first time have emerged from the water to live on land. Plants, entirely different from those we know now, were then growing on land. Among them were all kinds of insects for the amphibians to eat.

About 200 million years ago another still higher stage of evolution was reached in the development of reptiles. These developed in a tremendous variety of types, from small to very large, living in the water and on land, with even flying forms occurring. Present-day turtles, lizards, snakes and crocodiles give us some idea of this animal group, which was then dominant.

About 70 million years ago the reptiles were pushed out

of their dominant position by the new groups of birds and mammals. These types, which also soon divided into numerous subtypes, were different from all preceding animals in that they were warm-blooded, that is to say, they had mechanisms enabling them to maintain their body temperature at a constant level. As a result, they were less dependent on differences and changes in climate, and their tissues and organs could function much more evenly. In other respects too they stood out above the earlier animals. They exhibit all kinds of complicated patterns of behavior such as those associated with nest building, selecting a mate, having social relationships within a group, and caring for the young. Moreover, they have at their disposal a striking variety of means of communication, including colors and patterns, songs and other sounds, gestures and postures. Among the mammals the group of the so-called primates is very important indeed. It is made up of the prosimians, monkeys and anthropoid apes, man being classified with this latter group.

In order to see clearly the position of man one must, as it were, get a bird's eye view of the entire development we have sketched. In a process that took billions of years, we see how the initially uninhabited earth gradually became populated. Step by step the ladder was climbed to the ever higher possibilities that lay hidden in creation. First, organic matter, then very simple forms of life, then plants; after that animals that could observe with their senses, then the successively higher structured types of vertebrate animals, with brains which became bigger and bigger, and more and more complex, and with behavior patterns that became ever richer and more varied.

Then, at the end of this long evolution, within creation, from a branch of the primates, there emerges man, a creature who lives on an entirely new level.

Just as from a plant, after months of growing and branching, a bud emerges and gradually grows bigger until one day a wondrously colored flower appears, so man also becomes the summit of creation. He not only has senses with which he can observe all kinds of things, but he can also think about the reality all about him, and about himself; he can draw conclusions, he can imagine the future, and make plans. He can take objects that he finds or seeks, like stones or bones, and deliberately alter them to suit them for a specific action, especially for self-defense and for obtaining food. In addition, he can speak and make languages with innumerable words to symbolize concepts, so that he is able to think and work with his fellow creatures, to share experiences, and to transmit these, especially to younger generations. By using and shaping and making artifacts he can not only enlarge, strengthen and make dexterous his hands — which are in themselves remarkable enough — but he can also change his immediate environment by making clothing and housing. With fire he can heat his dwelling and prepare food to suit his taste.

In short, at the end of the long process of evolution a ruling creature appears on earth who has the real potential for subjecting this earthly reality, including his fellow organisms, to himself. But what especially characterizes this creature is his freedom, his capacity always to choose one course of action from among several possibilities. Consequently, his behavior is governed far less by fixed structured patterns than is the case with the animals. He must therefore consider and choose before he does anything, and as he observes the consequences of his actions he learns that one choice is preferable to another. On the basis of his experience he forms rules for his conduct, which in turn become norms within the context of freedom. As such his laws differ in character from those to which animal behavior responds.

A number of other considerations play a role in the development of these norms. Man is conscious of his existence. He experiences the temporality of the life of organisms and of his own life; he observes the breaking down in his own body as he grows older; he sees and experiences illness and accident. Also in the relationships between individuals and groups there are tensions and conflicts that often lead to the disruption, curtailment, and even destruction of human life. All these experiences lead man on to ask questions about the meaning of his existence in all of its aspects, of the origin and of the meaning of the remarkable reality in which he finds himself. Thus in man this earthly reality has fully awakened. Now comes the highest characteristic of man: he stands, as it were, face to face with the Creator of this earthly reality. Thus man can become aware who gave him the task of ruling the world, and who placed him in this responsible position.

Out of this long chain of evolution lasting billions of years there was finally born this amazing creature, one in whom this earthly reality has come to stand openly before God. Evolution thus terminated in this revelatory encounter with God. In this awareness of God as his maker man should have carried out his task. From the very beginning of man's history, from the very first human beings, however, this was not the case. Usually, man has used his freedom to rule in wrong ways. His highest allegiance has been to himself, to things in created reality, to his own systems of thought; these are his highest values, his gods, which determine the norms in his domain of freedom.

However, before we consider this subject more fully, let us first trace the further course of man's development.

VIII: THE DOMINION OF MAN

IN THE LAST CHAPTER WE TRACED THE EVOLUTION AND UNFOLD-ing of creation from the time the earth was uninhabited by living organisms through the successive phases of the formation of the plant and animal kingdoms to the birth of that most marvelous creature, man. That was, however, by no means the end of the development of this earthly reality; in fact, it was continued on an entirely new level in mankind. Now it was no longer a biological development, but rather the unfolding of latent potentialities in man of a wholly different kind.

Let us now try to get a bird's eye view of this phase. In your picture of reality — this cannot be emphasized too strongly — you should regard these developments as the continuation of the phases of evolution that we have discussed earlier. I now invite you to join me in the difficult but most rewarding attempt to oversee the entire development of this earthly reality at a single glance. Unless you succeed in this, you will miss something that is most beautiful, illuminating, and essential.

At first man lived in groups. He acquired his food by hunting animals, but also by eating fruits and roots. One could say that in this first stage, which lasted hundreds of thousands of years, the presence of man on earth was really not very noticeable; that is, man's influence on his environment, on the landscape and on his fellow creatures, was extremely small, and not very different from that of the higher primates. In our mind's eye we must visualize man as having spread very soon over practically all of the so-called ancient world: Africa, Asia, and Europe.

48

After the last ice age, about ten to twenty thousand years ago, man's influence on the earth became greater, especially when he began to grow crops and to raise cattle in various places. On a small scale man was beginning to subject nature to himself. For agriculture suitable areas had to be cultivated and planted with selected grains. In this way, comparatively speaking, large quantities of nonperishable food were obtained. As a result larger numbers of people could live together in a fixed abode. Thus cities and states arose, and people developed a more stable form of life. This in turn offered new possibilities for the further development of culture. A division of labor now became possible. Some people took care of the food production, others devoted themselves to making tools, weapons, furniture, clothing, and buildings. A differentiation in trades developed, and at the same time class distinctions — differences in social classes — appeared. Alongside the craftsmen, there developed the machinery of government, mostly with a ruler at the head and officials, for example, to levy and collect taxes for general services. A caste of priests also arose, whose task it was to channel and to give form to the expression of religious emotions.

In short, a new phase of evolution was reached in which civilizations arose in various places on several continents. In their thinking, their ideology or life and world view, men were governed by very different religions, which were, moreover, often very local in character. Everywhere the people revered gods, which, as we have previously seen, were often things from within this earthly reality: heavenly bodies, plants, animals, human beings, etc. These local gods, so the people believed, determined their weal and woe. Nature, including human life, was subject to the unpredictable whims of the gods, which one could only hope to appease with sacrifices, often of a most horrible kind.

In these civilizations other capacities of man also began to flower. The religions and rulers stimulated artists and architects to erect temples and palaces and cities full of beauty and splendor. Here and there we also see the beginnings of activities in the natural sciences, particularly in the areas of medicine, mathematics, and astronomy, the latter, however, permeated with religious motifs. The art of writing also developed.

In our overall view of this development we do well to bear in mind that these civilizations, which were very much alike in their general characteristics, arose in different places. And it often happened that a civilization, after flourishing for a time, would lose its forward impetus, and gradually or even abruptly be succeeded by another. However, the level of civilization attained generally did not vary a great deal.

The European civilization, in which Greek, Roman, Jewish and Christian influences gradually merged, at first manifested the same features as did other civilizations. Indeed, during the middle ages the European picture of reality, philosophy, religion, and social relations threatened to run dead in a single, rigid, static system. Yet today — some five hundred years later — this civilization, or at least many aspects of it, has spread over the entire earth. This is something that did not happen in the case of earlier civilizations.

European civilization spread because of a new breakthrough, a new phase of the long development we have been tracing. The great pacemaker on this new level of evolution has been natural science. Its principle was discovered by the founders of modern astronomy and physics during the sixteenth and seventeenth centuries. At that time people started making exact observations and doing experiments in the area of mechanics. For example, they observed and measured moving objects. These movements, they discovered, exhibited a regularity that could be expressed in mathematical formulas. Knowing these laws, they could make predictions, for example, about the course of planets. It was in this period, then, that the first elements of our modern picture of reality, such as the movement of the earth around the sun, were being formed.

This discovery of the scientific method had two important consequences. First of all, it was soon realized that one could not only obtain interesting information about the physical aspects of reality in this way, but also that this knowledge had technological applications. Men could begin to build machines. And thus the scientific method, together with the parallel development of technology, has led in an unbroken path to modern physics, industrialization, and to our present society with its cars, airplanes, electricity, radio, and television.

A second consequence was the application of these pro-
ductive principles during the past two centuries to the
areas of chemistry, geology, and biology. Here too man
began to study the phenomena exactly, experiments were
performed in specific ways, equipment of ever greater com-
plexity was used, and the attempt made to express the laws
of science mathematically.

As a result of this development twentieth-century man has
increasingly come to know and control the inanimate matter
of this earthly reality. Clear evidence of this we find, for
example, in atomic reactors, in space flight, in great power
dams. In addition, man is beginning to gain so much insight
into life processes — our knowledge in this area grows faster
each passing year — that the possibilities for the technical
control of life now appear to be nearly unlimited.

From the nomadic tribes, who lived hundreds of thousands of years ago among their fellow beings without leaving
many traces, there has emerged a mankind that has not only
drastically altered large parts of the earth's surface, split
atoms, sent recording apparatus through the solar system,
but which also has the potential for radically altering life
processes. Just as developments in physics and technology
often leave us bewildered, so at the present time in biology
scientists are busy unravelling and analyzing, in a manner
that shocks us, the elementary threads of life, the proteins
and nucleic acids. These, as we have already seen, are the
chemical substances in which our inherited characteristics
are fixed, and which determine all the cell processes to
which organisms conform. Moreover, in biology we now also
have knowledge about many of the factors that guided evolution in the past, about those which determine the relations
between the species and the numbers of individuals, and
about the regulatory mechanisms — the nervous system and
the hormones — that function in the body. Fascinating investigations have also been initiated into the learning
processes and memory, and consequently also into the functioning of our brains.

The new phase to which this earthly reality has come
since the rise of modern science is therefore characterized
by the fact that its highest component, man, is now busy
analyzing, learning to know, and especially to control, this

reality, its inanimate components, the plants and animals, and himself.

This shocks us most when we realize that for some time now this marvelous creature has been applying his knowledge in repairing his own body. Until recently this took the form of swallowing or injecting certain chemicals, and the removal of defective parts through surgery, but nowadays worn-out organs are being replaced by artificial ones or by organs from fellow human beings, living or dead.

Through his knowledge of life processes man has been able to improve all kinds of organisms for the benefit of agriculture, horticulture, and animal husbandry, and to combat harmful organisms, so that food production has shown an amazing increase. At the same time man has been able to considerably lengthen the average life span through his increased knowledge and technology.

The consequences of this development in the natural sciences are even more far reaching. Through the production of contraceptives and other means, man possesses in principle the means of determining the size of future generations. We can, if desired, determine exactly how many people shall be born in the future. The so-called quality of the coming generations is also increasingly becoming a matter of technical control.

In summary, we are living in the midst of a transition to an entirely new period, in which man will know and control in a very detailed and fundamental manner the functioning of matter, the inanimate environment on the earth, and in part even outside of it, of living creatures, and of himself. Increasingly, man holds in his hands the future development of this earthly reality.

This transition brings with it entirely new and extremely critical problems, problems that were never confronted by former generations. Recall not only what has been said about birth control and organ transplants, but also about atomic weapons, which are capable of bringing to an end the entire development we have here discussed. Or think of the serious pollution of the earth's surface and atmosphere by insecticides and waste products. Consider the problems raised by artificial insemination in man, by reanimation, by scientifically administered brainwashing, and the like. No one will say that these problems are only scientific and technological. The deepest questions to which the modern development of the natural sciences and technology have given rise are ethical and ideological.

In the first chapter of the Bible we read about the role given to man on earth by his Creator: "Be fruitful and multiply, fill the earth and subdue it, and have dominion over the fish of the sea and over the birds of the air, and over every living thing that moves upon the earth" (Gen. 1:28).

In the past few decades these words have been fulfilled in a dramatic, never to be suspected manner. Will we, the people of the present phase, be able to use our ever increasing power to good ends (indeed, what does *good* mean in this context?) or will we misuse it bringing about impoverishment, degeneration, slavery on an unprecedented scale, or even total destruction?

IX: THE ANSWER

EVERYTHING WE HAVE DISCUSSED SO FAR — OUR MODERN science-oriented picture of the origin of the world as spanning a period of billions of years and our desire to understand the message of the Bible as correctly as possible — culminates in and leads to the question: What is man's role in the present world and what are his prospects for the future? Which way must man turn in the present situation, which is so enormously complicated, so full of problems and tensions, and which he has, at least in part, brought upon himself?

We have already seen that the modern development of natural science — its methods are increasingly being followed in the other sciences — carried the process of evolution to a higher level. That was undeniably a good thing. But we also saw that the greatest problems now confronting us are ethical and ideological in character. Our knowledge has increased tremendously, but what must we do with this knowledge?

In today's world different answers are being given to this question.

In this concluding chapter we shall attempt to give a very definite answer. I know that the central thrust of this answer is right, simply because I believe in it. My formulation of the answer, I am aware, will be imperfect despite my best efforts.

The subject, then, is again man. In order to have the proper perspective on man we must first call attention to still another facet of this primate. Man displays a great resemblance to other organisms not only in his most fundamental cell processes and body structure, but also in his behavior. This can readily be elucidated with a few examples.

Man employs objects to do and make things, but often animals do likewise. Birds build nests; beavers build dams from branches and gnawed down tree trunks in order to regulate the water level in rivers and ponds; certain animals use stones to pry open hard plant seeds or to cut open their prey; others use sticks to get at inaccessible food. Consider also human speech. Speech is species specific, that is, peculiar to man, but it must be added that many animals also employ sounds in communicating. What is of even greater interest and importance is the fact that many features of human speech also occur in the animals, especially those which are emotional in nature, and which often determine the tone and tenor of our words. Learning capacity, which plays such a great role in our life, occurs at a lower level, with much variation, in numerous animals.

There are many types of behavior that we partially share with the animals. When gorillas awaken in the morning on the bed of leaves they have made for themselves, they yawn and stretch themselves. When they are sitting on a branch, they dangle their legs. Sometimes they rest on their backs with their front paws folded beneath their heads. When irritated they knit their brows; when insecure they bite their lips. They will bow to an opponent of their species who is of a higher rank, similar to the way we nod the head when we greet a person. Similarly, handshaking occurs among chimpanzees. Reactions such as screaming, throwing objects, slamming doors, which we witness among people in conflict situations, also occur among the anthropoid apes.

When one takes cognizance of all this modern knowledge about animal behavior, he comes to the amazing conclusion that much of human behavior, like the human body, is reminiscent of man's origins in the animal kingdom.

Of special interest are the many investigations dealing with the territory of animals. During the mating and reproduction period, when the young are being born and fed, many animals will occupy a certain territory and defend it against other animals of their species. Equally important is the discovery that there is quite often a hierarchy when animals live in social groups.

And thus the conviction has grown that these behavior patterns, which are so deeply rooted in the past, continue to play a fundamental role in our society, for example, in the ownership of property (especially of land and living space), in the arrangement of our homes, in social regulations, in the division of our day, in business, competition, and advertising, in mass demonstrations, questions about authority, and the like.

The phenomenon of aggression has also received a good deal of attention in recent writings. In biology the term aggression especially refers to threatening and aggressive behavior among animals of the same species. The remarkable thing is that among animals such behavior seldom results in serious injury or death.

Consider for a moment the fact that in the past 150 years an estimated 60 million people have lost their lives in wars and in concentration camps. There have been frequent episodes of torture, deliberate maiming, burning, and cannibalism in the history of mankind. The spotlight focused on the aggression of the human species is enough to make us shudder. People used to speak of "the bestial in man" to refer to our animal origins. Nowadays we have come to regard this "bestiality" rather as a typically human trait. It is very likely that the employment of weapons has always been a characteristic of the human species, for the human body is so vulnerable, so lacking in means of defense like claws and fangs. Moreover, because we are carnivorous in origin, we could only stay alive by means of weapons such as bones and sticks and stones. However, in fights among members of our species the blow given all too frequently comes too hard. In many human fossils there are traces that indicate that the person did not die a natural death. In modern warfare this aggressive characteristic of man has been put on a scientific basis and carried through to its most awful consequences.

Before discussing further this perplexing discovery about our species, let us look at another matter that is crucial to our final conclusion. The discovery in the natural sciences that man can experiment with and control nature has given rise to, or at least stimulated, the conviction that this also is true for society. Social relationships, natural units, political alignments, and ecclesiastical structures, which were long regarded as static, are now being analyzed critically and tested as to their worth and genuineness. The consequence of this critical examination has been the development of a heightened sense of responsibility in the individual, a desire to have a voice, to participate in decision making about work, church, education, government, and the large questions of poverty and riches, of war and peace.

What is the origin of the abuses that exist in society and between peoples and nations? The answer to this question is really very simple. We have seen that man's task is the governing of this earthly reality. This is an innate characteristic of man, given with creation. Now when the individual man saw a chance to benefit himself by exercising dominion, the governing function, also over a fellow human being, he did so. What is true for the individual also holds for the group. Accordingly, despots and pirates arose, one people or race subjugated another, slavery started, colonies were acquired, there came to be rich people and poor, and people strove and indeed continue to strive to enslave others by imposing upon them systems of thought, ideologies, and even religions, while denying to them the right to hold or express opinions of their own. Throughout all of history, to the present day, we see this primitive, specifically human aggression drive functioning again and again, resorting to weapons to achieve its aims.

With the modern development of the natural sciences man's potential for dominating inanimate nature and plant, animal, and human life has increased very greatly, opening perspectives on the future which are extremely auspicious, but which can also be fatal in their application. Fortunately, in our time we are becoming increasingly aware that human society too is in great need of improvement, so that each individual, in accordance with his native potentials, may share equally in the realization of these perspectives.

In this world in which the natural sciences, technology, and medicine have brought about such great changes, which is confronted with such great ethical and ideological problems, in which social and political shifts are occurring, in which members of the same species, armed to the teeth, stand opposing each other, in which there are such great tensions between the races, in which very rich and very poor nations and people dwell side by side, in this world with its history of development of approximately five billion years, in this world we also still find Christians.

For a long time Christendom, that portion of the world in which Christianity supposedly prevails, was not very clear about the role it could and should play in the development of mankind. In many respects it acted as a deterrent in the early development of the modern sciences. Christians insisted that the sun revolved around the earth; Christians opposed the idea of evolution. And not only did Christendom cling tenaciously to an antiquated picture of reality, but it also identified itself with the established, conservative view of social and community relations. It often sanctioned social abuses. What is more, Christendom often lost credibility because of its pernicious splintering into sectarian groups.

However, despite ourselves, we are now beginning to realize with amazement and trepidation that if ever there was a time in which the gospel of our Lord Jesus Christ is relevant, it is ours. The more our knowledge of the reality about us increases, the more clearly we understand that we are living in a world that is caught up in an all-embracing process of evolution. The more deeply we learn to know man and ourselves, the more clearly we begin to see that Christ's message can really assist us in our search for solutions to the great problems of today and tomorrow.

For Christ teaches us the universal equality of all men without distinction of race or color. Christ teaches us social concern, love of neighbor, peaceableness and personal responsibility. Following him therefore means the arresting of aggression in all its forms, and the realization that brute force should be replaced by a real solidarity, each of us being prepared to make sacrifices to his fellow man.

In Jesus, who has proved his teaching by his life and death, God, the creator of this entire reality, comes to mankind in a wondrous manner. He desires in forgiveness to liberate us from the evil that we individually and collectively have brought about on the earth, and he shows us a new way, the only right way.

When you gaze at the stars some dark night, the stars that

are so infinitely far away, and think back to all the generations that have lived on this earth since life first moved in the oceans billions of years ago and realize that all of this reality rests in the creative hands of God, and you worry and wonder about the conditions in the world today, and in your own short life, and ask again and again *Where are we headed?* then there is, I believe, but one answer.